Louis Moyse Flute Collection

Moyse Collection of Intermediate Flute Classics

WITH TWO COMPANION CDs

Recorded by Caen Thomason-Redus, flute
and Jeannie Yu, piano

ISBN: 978-1-4234-8280-2

G. SCHIRMER, Inc.

DISTRIBUTED BY

HAL•LEONARD®
CORPORATION

7777 W. BLUEMOUND RD. P.O. BOX 13819 MILWAUKEE, WI 53213

www.schirmer.com
www.halleonard.com

LOUIS MOYSE (1912-2007)

The leading flute teacher of the twentieth century, Louis Moyse (pronounced mo-EEZ) was born in the Netherlands in 1912 while his parents were on a European tour. His father, Marcel Moyse, was a renowned French flute player that toured extensively world-wide, gave master classes, taught privately, and wrote several method books on flute playing. Louis learned to play the flute and piano expertly from his father, and chose to focus on the flute by the time of his acceptance into the Paris Conservatory. In 1932, he won the Premier Prix at the conservatory and began assisting his father, who was on the faculty.

In the late 1930s, Moyse was appointed second chair flute of the Boston Symphony. Before he could make the journey from France, the outbreak of World War II caused borders to close. Moyse was not able to take the position and spent the next few years in France performing on piano with his wife and father in the Moyse Trio. The group left France following the war and journeyed to the United States after some time in South America.

In the United States, the trio settled in Vermont and began teaching at Marlboro College. Joined by European friends Rudolf Serkin, Adolf Busch, and Hermann Busch, the sextet founded the Marlboro Music School and Festival. They envisioned a summer series of workshops without an instructor or coach. Instead, seasoned musicians play alongside less experienced musicians and pass along valuable tips through making music together. Moyse remained involved in this organization for many years, performing with and encouraging thousands of young musicians. He and his first wife, in the early 1950s formed the Brattleboro Music Center, now called the New England Bach Festival.

For the next several decades, Moyse taught at Boston University and the University of Toronto, and coached hundreds of students at the Marlboro Music Festival, and in master classes. From his Vermont home, Moyse instructed scores of students privately, composed and arranged nearly two hundred works, coached ensembles, led master classes, and edited many volumes of flute literature. The significance of his contribution to flute pedagogy in the twentieth century cannot be overstated. His editions have become the staple of nearly every flute studio and have come to define what is considered appropriate repertoire for the instrument. His master classes and ensemble coaching sessions were much coveted events attended regularly by students from around the world. Many of his private students are distinguished touring musicians and hold positions in the foremost orchestras. Moyse died at the age of 94 in 2007 of heart failure.

CONTENTS

ABOUT THE PERFORMERS

Caen Thomason-Redus, flute

Caen Thomason-Redus is currently the Assistant Professor of Flute at the University of Wisconsin-Milwaukee where he is an active soloist and chamber musician. He is also a frequent guest artist performing everything from early music to contemporary African American repertoire to jazz. Prior to arriving in Milwaukee, Caen spent two years performing with the Detroit Symphony Orchestra as their Minority Fellow. Caen earned performance degrees from Rice University and the University of Redlands, did additional studies at the University of Michigan and the Mozarteum Akademie (Salzburg, Austria), and began his formal training in the Preparatory Program at the San Francisco Conservatory of Music. His primary instructors were Leone Buyse, Candice Palmberg and Yaada Weber, but through his participation in numerous festivals and fellowship programs, Caen also studied with many other inspiring flutists including Mark Sparks and Jeff Zook. Caen's previous teaching activities include faculty positions at Wayne State University and the Sphinx Preparatory Academy, both located in downtown Detroit. Caen and his wife, hornist Kristi Crago, served as principals in the Evansville Philharmonic Orchestra and as faculty at the University of Evansville in Indiana. Dedicated to education and musical outreach, Caen and Kristi spend much of their personal time creating and taking part in programs that bring music closer to people of all backgrounds and ages.

Jeannie Yu, piano

Jeannie Yu was awarded first prize in the Frinna Awerbuch Piano Competition in New York, the Flint Symphony International Concerto Competition, the Portland Symphony International Concerto Competition, and the Kingsville Piano Competition in Texas. She also earned the prestigious Gina Bachauer Memorial Scholarship Award, a full scholarship to The Juilliard School of Music for both the bachelor and master's degree programs, and was awarded an accompanist fellowship at the Peabody Conservatory of Music where she received her Doctor of Musical Arts Degree.

Ms. Yu has performed as soloist with the Flint Symphony, Portland Symphony, Marina del Rey-Westchester Symphony, Des Moines Symphony, Des Moines Brandenburg Symphony, the Xiamen Symphony Orchestra in China, and the Milwaukee Ballet Orchestra. She has been in great demand as a soloist and collaborative artist in live performances on WQXR in New York, WOI in Iowa, and chamber music concerts such as the Northwestern University Winter Chamber Music Series and the Rembrandt Chamber Players Series in Chicago. She also performs as a member of the Florestan Duo and the Kneisel Trio.

Ms. Yu has also served on the faculty of Alfred University Summer Chamber Music Institute, the Ohio Wesleyan Summer Chamber Music Festival, the Milwaukee Chamber Music Festival, and the Troy Youth Chamber Music Institute.

Aria

Transcribed by Louis Moyse

Joachim Andersen
(1847–1909)

Sonata No. 4 in C Major
for Flute and Basso Continuo, BWV 1033

Realization by Louis Moyse

Johann Sebastian Bach
(1685–1750)

* All trills should start on the
note above and on the beat.

Menuett I

Menuett II

Da capo Menuett I

Rêverie

Transcribed by Louis Moyse

Claude Debussy
(1862–1918)

Tempo I

Berceuse
from *Dolly*, Op. 56, No. 1

Transcribed by Louis Moyse

Gabriel Fauré
(1845–1924)

Sonata in F Major
Op. 1, No. 11

Realization by Louis Moyse

George Frideric Handel
(1685–1759)

* The bracketed two bars are not in the Urtext. They have been inserted by the editor, who feels they are necessary for a balanced ending of the movement.

Allegro
second movement from Sonata No. 3 in A Major
for Piano, Violin (or Flute), and Violoncello, K. 12

Wolfgang Amadeus Mozart
(1756–1791)

* Before the beat

Allegro spiritoso
first movement from Concerto in G Major

Giovanni Battista Pergolesi
(1710–1736)

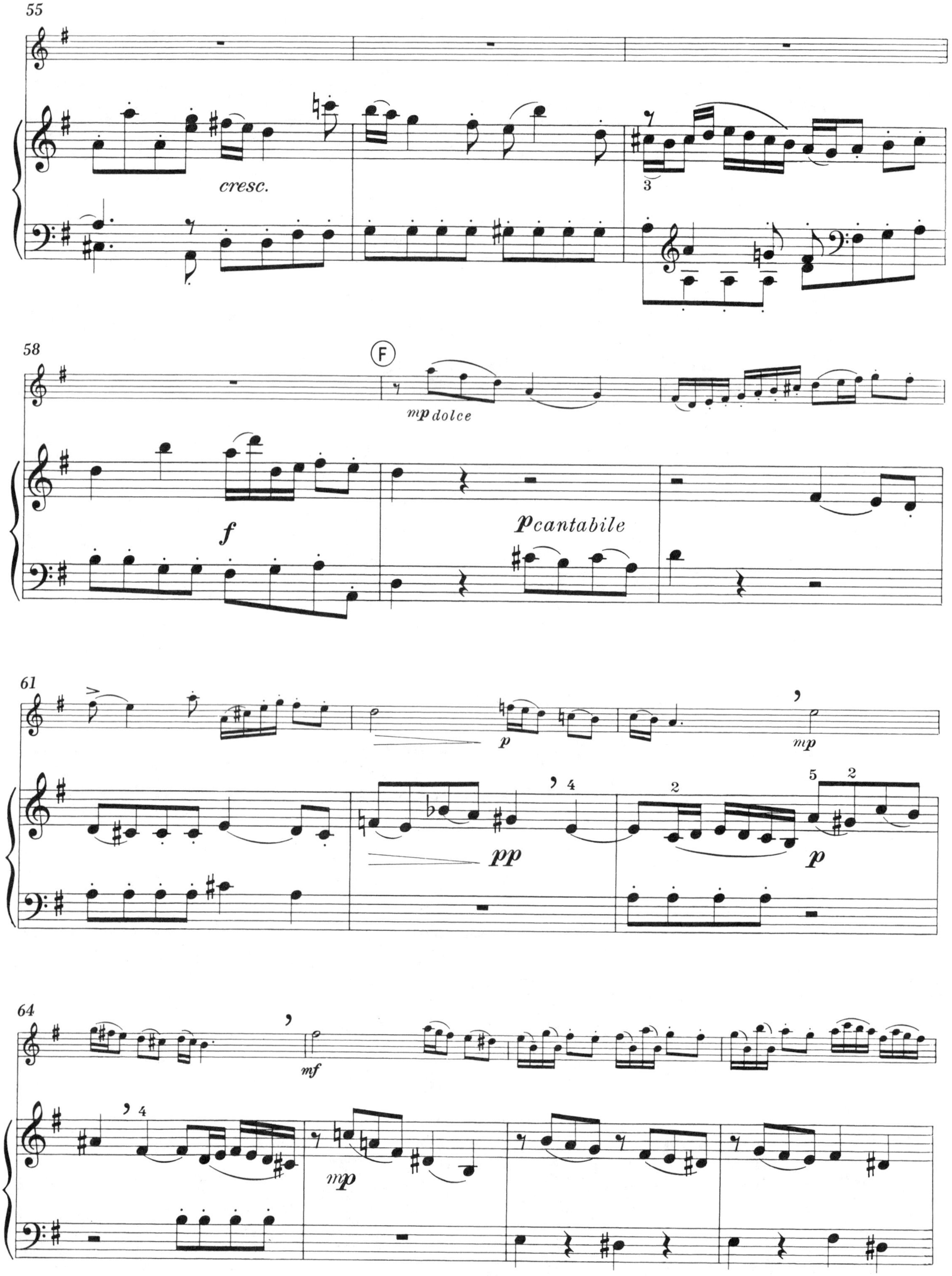
55
cresc.
58
F
mp dolce
f
p cantabile
61
p
mp
pp
p
64
mf
mp

Moment Musical
from 6 *Momens musicals*, D. 780

Transcribed by Louis Moyse

Franz Schubert
(1797–1828)

Romanze
from *Drei Romanzen*, Op. 94

Transcribed by Louis Moyse

Robert Schumann
(1810–1856)

Simplice, affettuoso

Sonatina in F Major

Transcribed by Louis Moyse

I

Georg Philipp Telemann
(1681–1767)

Vivace

II

III

The Fifers
(Les Fifres)
from *Quatrième Suite* of *Pieces de Clavecin, Première Livre*

Transcribed by Louis Moyse

Jean-François Dandrieu
(c.1681–1738)

Vif et légèrement

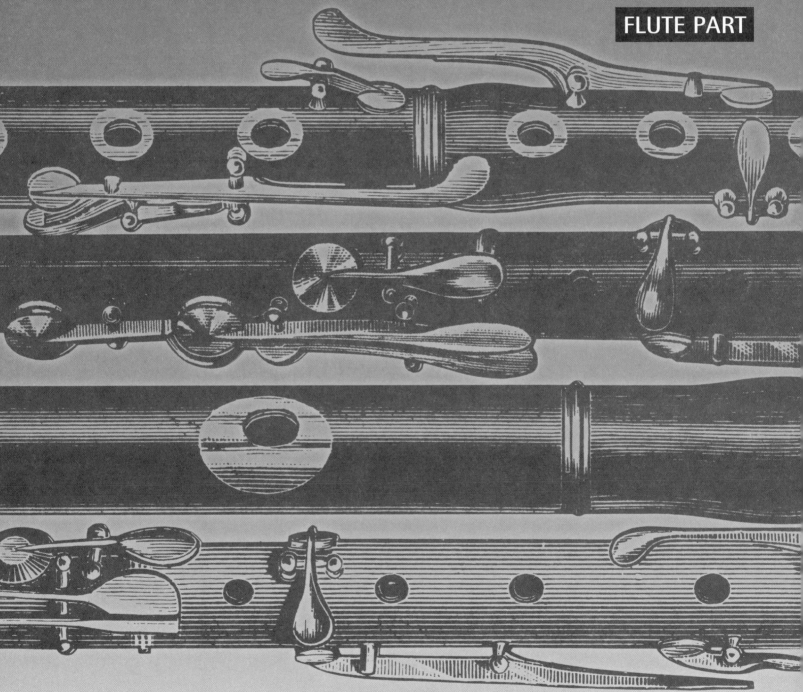

Louis Moyse Flute Collection

Moyse Collection of Intermediate Flute Classics

FLUTE PART

ISBN: 978-1-4234-8280-2

G. SCHIRMER, Inc.

DISTRIBUTED BY

HAL•LEONARD®
CORPORATION
7777 W. BLUEMOUND RD. P.O. BOX 13819 MILWAUKEE, WI 53213

www.schirmer.com
www.halleonard.com

CONTENTS

LOUIS MOYSE (1912-2007)

The leading flute teacher of the twentieth century, Louis Moyse (pronounced mo-EEZ) was born in the Netherlands in 1912 while his parents were on a European tour. His father, Marcel Moyse, was a renowned French flute player that toured extensively world-wide, gave master classes, taught privately, and wrote several method books on flute playing. Louis learned to play the flute and piano expertly from his father, and chose to focus on the flute by the time of his acceptance into the Paris Conservatory. In 1932, he won the Premier Prix at the conservatory and began assisting his father, who was on the faculty.

In the late 1930s, Moyse was appointed second chair flute of the Boston Symphony. Before he could make the journey from France, the outbreak of World War II caused borders to close. Moyse was not able to take the position and spent the next few years in France performing on piano with his wife and father in the Moyse Trio. The group left France following the war and journeyed to the United States after some time in South America.

In the United States, the trio settled in Vermont and began teaching at Marlboro College. Joined by European friends Rudolf Serkin, Adolf Busch, and Hermann Busch, the sextet founded the Marlboro Music School and Festival. They envisioned a summer series of workshops without an instructor or coach. Instead, seasoned musicians play alongside less experienced musicians and pass along valuable tips through making music together. Moyse remained involved in this organization for many years, performing with and encouraging thousands of young musicians. He and his first wife, in the early 1950s formed the Brattleboro Music Center, now called the New England Bach Festival.

For the next several decades, Moyse taught at Boston University and the University of Toronto, and coached hundreds of students at the Marlboro Music Festival, and in master classes. From his Vermont home, Moyse instructed scores of students privately, composed and arranged nearly two hundred works, coached ensembles, led master classes, and edited many volumes of flute literature. The significance of his contribution to flute pedagogy in the twentieth century cannot be overstated. His editions have become the staple of nearly every flute studio and have come to define what is considered appropriate repertoire for the instrument. His master classes and ensemble coaching sessions were much coveted events attended regularly by students from around the world. Many of his private students are distinguished touring musicians and hold positions in the foremost orchestras. Moyse died at the age of 94 in 2007 of heart failure.

Caen Thomason-Redus, flute

Caen Thomason-Redus is currently the Assistant Professor of Flute at the University of Wisconsin-Milwaukee where he is an active soloist and chamber musician. He is also a frequent guest artist performing everything from early music to contemporary African American repertoire to jazz. Prior to arriving in Milwaukee, Caen spent two years performing with the Detroit Symphony Orchestra as their Minority Fellow. Caen earned performance degrees from Rice University and the University of Redlands, did additional studies at the University of Michigan and the Mozarteum Akademie (Salzburg, Austria), and began his formal training in the Preparatory Program at the San Francisco Conservatory of Music. His primary instructors were Leone Buyse, Candice Palmberg and Yaada Weber, but through his participation in numerous festivals and fellowship programs, Caen also studied with many other inspiring flutists including Mark Sparks and Jeff Zook. Caen's previous teaching activities include faculty positions at Wayne State University and the Sphinx Preparatory Academy, both located in downtown Detroit. Caen and his wife, hornist Kristi Crago, served as principals in the Evansville Philharmonic Orchestra and as faculty at the University of Evansville in Indiana. Dedicated to education and musical outreach, Caen and Kristi spend much of their personal time creating and taking part in programs that bring music closer to people of all backgrounds and ages.

Jeannie Yu, piano

Jeannie Yu was awarded first prize in the Frinna Awerbuch Piano Competition in New York, the Flint Symphony International Concerto Competition, the Portland Symphony International Concerto Competition, and the Kingsville Piano Competition in Texas. She also earned the prestigious Gina Bachauer Memorial Scholarship Award, a full scholarship to The Juilliard School of Music for both the bachelor and master's degree programs, and was awarded an accompanist fellowship at the Peabody Conservatory of Music where she received her Doctor of Musical Arts Degree.

Ms. Yu has performed as soloist with the Flint Symphony, Portland Symphony, Marina del Rey-Westchester Symphony, Des Moines Symphony, Des Moines Brandenburg Symphony, the Xiamen Symphony Orchestra in China, and the Milwaukee Ballet Orchestra. She has been in great demand as a soloist and collaborative artist in live performances on WQXR in New York, WOI in Iowa, and chamber music concerts such as the Northwestern University Winter Chamber Music Series and the Rembrandt Chamber Players Series in Chicago. She also performs as a member of the Florestan Duo and the Kneisel Trio.

Ms. Yu has also served on the faculty of Alfred University Summer Chamber Music Institute, the Ohio Wesleyan Summer Chamber Music Festival, the Milwaukee Chamber Music Festival, and the Troy Youth Chamber Music Institute.

6

Sonata No. 4 in C Major
for Flute and Basso Continuo, BWV 1033

Realization by Louis Moyse

Johann Sebastian Bach
(1685–1750)

The pianist plays the following as an introduction on the accompaniment track:

The pianist plays the following as an introduction on the accompaniment track:

8

Adagio

p espressivo

mp   *cresc.*

f   *p*

cresc.   *molto*   *rit. tr*   *f*

The pianist plays the following as an introduction on the accompaniment track:

Menuett I

p

mp   *poco cresc.*   *mf*

Menuett II

p dolce

p

cresc.   *mf*

pp   *cresc.*

mf

Da capo Menuett I

The pianist plays measures 13-16 as an introduction on the accompaniment track.

Aria

Transcribed by Louis Moyse

Moderato

Joachim Andersen
(1847–1909)

The pianist plays measures 7-8 as an introduction on the accompaniment track.

The Fifers

(Les Fifres)

from *Quatrième Suite* of *Pieces de Clavecin, Première Livre*

Jean-François Dandrieu
(c.1681–1738)

Transcribed by Louis Moyse

Vif et légèrement

The pianist plays measures 5-8 as an introduction on the accompaniment track.

Rêverie

Transcribed by Louis Moyse

Claude Debussy
(1862–1918)

Berceuse
from *Dolly*, Op. 56, No. 1

Transcribed by Louis Moyse

Gabriel Fauré
(1845–1924)

Andantino moderato

Sonata in F Major
Op. 1, No. 11

Realization by Louis Moyse

George Frideric Handel
(1685–1759)

The pianist plays the following as an introduction on the accompaniment track:

The pianist plays the following as an introduction on the accompaniment track:

14

* The bracketed two bars are not in the Urtext. They have been inserted by the editor, who feels they are necessary for a balanced ending of the movement.

The pianist plays the following as an introduction on the accompaniment track:

Romanze
from *Drei Romanzen*, Op. 94

Transcribed by Louis Moyse

Robert Schumann
(1810–1856)

Semplice, affettuoso

The pianist plays the following as an introduction on the accompaniment track:

Allegro
second movement from Sonata No. 3 in A Major
for Piano, Violin (or Flute), and Violoncello, K. 12

Wolfgang Amadeus Mozart
(1756–1791)

The pianist plays the following as an introduction on the accompaniment track:

18

Allegro spiritoso
first movement from Concerto in G Major

Giovanni Battista Pergolesi
(1710–1736)

Moment Musical

from 6 *Momens musicals*, D. 780

Transcribed by Louis Moyse

Franz Schubert
(1797–1828)

Sonatina in F Major

Transcribed by Louis Moyse

I

Georg Philipp Telemann
(1681–1767)

The pianist plays the following as an introduction on the accompaniment track:

II

Cantabile

The pianist plays the following as an introduction on the accompaniment track:

III

Presto

The pianist plays the following as an introduction on the accompaniment track:

ABOUT THE ENHANCED CDs

In addition to full performances and piano accompaniments playable on both your CD player and computer, these enhanced CDs also include tempo adjustment software for computer use only. This software, known as Amazing Slow Downer, was originally created for use in pop music to allow singers and players the freedom to independently adjust both tempo and pitch elements. Because we believe there may be valuable uses for these features in other musical genres, we have included this software as a tool for both the teacher and student. For quick and easy installation instructions of this software, please see below.

In recording a piano accompaniment we necessarily must choose one tempo. Our choice of tempo, phrasing, and dynamics is carefully considered. But by the nature of recording, it is only one option.

However, we encourage you to explore your own interpretive ideas, which may differ from our recordings. This software feature allows you to adjust the tempo up and down without affecting the pitch. We recommend that this tempo adjustment feature be used with care and insight.

The audio quality may be somewhat compromised when played through the Amazing Slow Downer. This compromise in quality will not be a factor in playing the CD audio track on a normal CD player or through another audio computer program.

INSTALLATION INSTRUCTIONS:

For Macintosh OS 8, 9, and X:
Load the CD-ROM into your CD-ROM Drive on your computer.
Each computer is set up a little differently. Your computer may automatically open the audio CD portion of this enhanced CD and begin to play it.
To access the CD-ROM features, double-click on the data portion of the CD-ROM (which will have the Hal Leonard icon in red and be named as the book).
Double-click on the "Amazing OS 8 (9 or X)" folder.
Double-click "Amazing Slow Downer"/"Amazing X PA" to run the software from the CD-ROM, or copy this file to your hard disk and run it from there.
Follow the instructions on-screen to get started. The Amazing Slow Downer should display tempo, pitch and mix bars. Click to select your track and adjust pitch or tempo by sliding the appropriate bar to the left or to the right.

For Windows:
Load the CD-ROM into your CD-ROM Drive on your computer.
Each computer is set up a little differently. Your computer may automatically open the audio CD portion of this enhanced CD and begin to play it.
To access the CD-ROM features, click on My Computer then right click on the Drive that you placed the CD in. Click Open. You should then see a folder named "Amazing Slow Downer". Click to open the "Amazing Slow Downer" folder.
Double-click "setup.exe" to install the software from the CD-ROM to your hard disk. Follow the on-screen instructions to complete installation.
Go to "Start," "Programs" and find the "Amazing Slow Downer" folder. Go to that folder and select the "Amazing Slow Downer" software.
Follow the instructions on-screen to get started. The Amazing Slow Downer should display tempo, pitch and mix bars. Click to select your track and adjust pitch or tempo by sliding the appropriate bar to the left or to the right.
Note: On Windows NT, 2000, XP, and Vista, the user should be logged in as the "Administrator" to guarantee access to the CD-ROM drive. Please see the help file for further information.

MINIMUM SYSTEM REQUIREMENTS:

For Macintosh:
Power Macintosh; Mac OS 8.5 or higher; 4 MB Application RAM; 8x Multi-Session CD-ROM drive

For Windows:
Pentium, Celeron or equivalent processor; Windows 95, 98, ME, NT, 2000, XP, Vista; 4 MB Application RAM; 8x Multi-Session CD-ROM drive